Custard Calamity

Written by Casey Elisha

Illustrated by Lhaiza Morena

Shola was going to play out on the grass with Tate and his puppy, Rosie. "Look after that hair!" called Shola's mum from the window.

Tate and Rosie were playing with a frisbee.

"You have a go," Tate said.

Shola sent the frisbee over to Rosie,

who was waiting for it.

"Hey, kids!" Ms Monroe called.

"I just got some fresh custard to have with a cake. Tell mums and dads that you can all come and have some!"

Rosie started running
to Ms Monroe and
the custard.

"Slow down, Rosie!" Tate and Shola called.

They tried to stop Rosie but it was too late.

Rosie jolted right into Ms Monroe!

The custard went flying and then ...

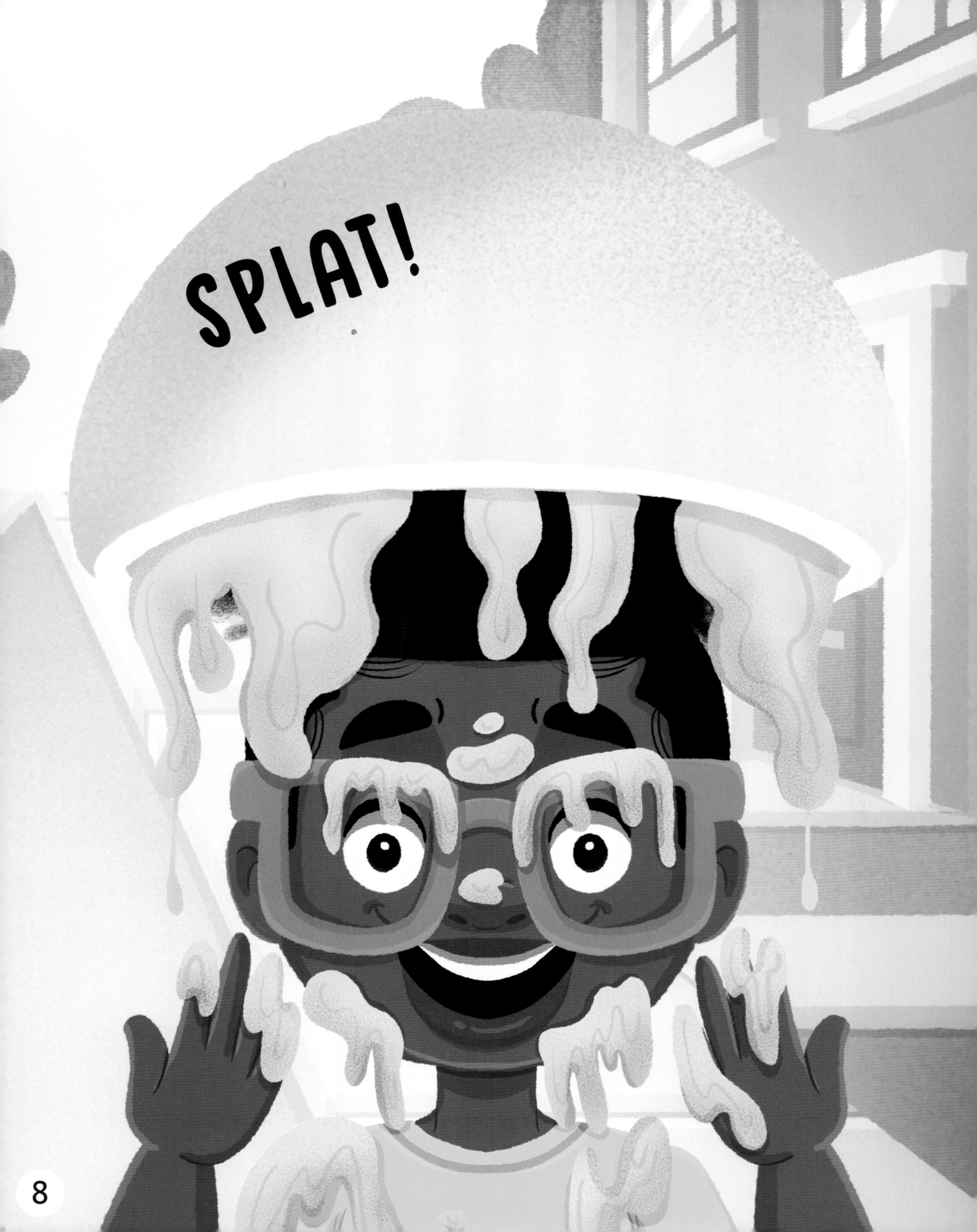
SPLAT!

The yellow mess landed on Shola and coated her hair! They all froze in shock.

Shola's mum was not happy!

"Tate, take Rosie home. Shola, we have to get you to the salon!"

Shola's mum got on the phone to the salon.

When they got there, Shola told the
hairdresser what went on.
"It is all right. I will look after you," she said.

The hairdresser added shampoo to Shola's hair again and again so it got clean and very soft.

Then she blow dried it and started styling it.

Shola looked in the mirror ...

"Wow!" she said.

Her hair was in braids with pink

and clear beads.

"It looks fantastic!"